"Mother Goose rhymed about it. Hippocrates taught it to his students. It helped a tiny tot in a Bethlehem manger get his first night of sleep. Even though it's been practiced by countless cultures for thousands of years, swaddling has become a lost art. All that's changing thanks to Raegan Moya-Jones, the Raphael of the swaddling renaissance. Swaddlelove illustrates what every parent needs to know: swaddling helps babies sleep soundly and for longer periods of time, and fosters that vital connection between parent and child. For the countless moms and dads who have seen 4:15 a.m. on the bedside clock one too many times, Swaddlelove — and a half dozen muslin wraps — just might change their lives."

— Shawn Bean , Senior Editor, *Babytalk Magazine*

swaddle love

raegan moya-jones

Damarae, Inc.
Brooklyn, NY

Photography by Michael Brian + Marko McPherson
Designed in the USA
Manufactured in China
Library of Congress Cataloging-in-Publication Date is available.

ISBN-13 978-0-9840599-0-4
ISBN-10 0-9840599-0-3

The photographs included in this book were taken for artistic purposes.
Please always put infants to sleep on their backs and be sure to avoid loose bedding
and soft sleeping surfaces.

Acknowledgements

+ + + + + + + + + + + +

I certainly took the road less traveled to publish this book.

The journey from being a mum who wanted to get the word out about swaddling to becoming the author of the book that you are holding in your hands right now was made possible by a small band of very smart, passionate, creative, and caring friends and family members who, above all, believed in me. To them I send my love and appreciation.

Thank you, Markos, David, Marie, Liz, Paula, Juliette, Cristina, Andrea, Paul, Pez, Frouds, Daniel, Ang, Lisa, Jen, Paigey, Mum, Dad, and Granty.

+ + + + + + + + + + +

For my earth angels,
Anais, Lourdes, and Arin—
all of whom make complete sense to me
when most other things around me don't.
And Markos,
without you none of this would be.
I love you all.

table of contents

introduction

I wrote this book for one reason: To tell you that swaddling is easy, helpful, and most important, essential.

As a mother of three who knows about the anxieties of parenting, I believe that anything I can do to make life easier for new parents, especially new mums, is a worthwhile endeavour. I decided that sharing what I know about swaddling with other mothers, fathers, and caregivers would be my tiny contribution to preserving their sanity during the first six months of their new baby's life, and helping the little one cope with his or her transition into this big wide world of ours.

There, I said it. I admitted to the world, and to you, dear reader, that whilst parenting will be one of the most blessed, eye-opening, and cherished parts of your life, it can also be one of the most confusing and chaotic.

If you are reading this book before the arrival of your first little one, brace yourself for the unexpected. I spent many a day with unwashed hair, eating cheese on toast for dinner, and crying more than I ever thought possible. In all honesty, I cried more during the first six months of my oldest daughter's life than I had in the previous 36 years before her arrival. A nurse told me that experts call the uncontrollable sobbing the "baby blues." I called it "why do I feel like this, and when will it stop?"

To make matters worse, Anais, our first daughter, was born the day before my birthday. As you probably suspect, I woke up the next morning in my hospital bed to see my husband sitting in the chair next to me with our new baby girl in his arms. It was obvious he had fallen in love with another woman, and the initial side effect of this was that it took him until about 6:00 that night to even remember that it was my birthday. I was reminded of my relegation to second string all day long, as I received call after call from family and friends, most of whom live in Australia, all congratulating me on the birth of my daughter, and all forgetting to include even a quick happy birthday wish. The main thought running through my head that day was, "and so it begins..."

How did I get from that first day to here, and how has this book come into being? Swaddling. To me, swaddling is nothing short of a godsend. It is a natural elixir for weary new parents who covet just one extra hour of sleep before they have to throw another load of laundry into the washer, run out for nappies, or take inventory of how much more breast milk to pump or formula to scoop. In a nutshell, swaddling helps your baby sleep longer and more peacefully, and that means you can sleep longer and deeper, and your household won't suffer from the kind of tension and disorder driven by sleep-deprived parents.

Contrary to what some new mums might tell you, swaddling is easy. It just takes a bit of practice and the right blanket, and swaddling will soon seem as natural to you as cuddling your baby. It's all about making your baby feel secure, and that's what mums and dads do best. Swaddling is one of the most endearing child-rearing practices that you will learn on your journey through parenthood, but it is sometimes misunderstood. Indeed, successful swaddling is more about consistency and

introduction

perseverance than precise techniques (although I've provided two quick and simple step-by-step techniques in Chapter 3).

Just think of swaddling as doing what comes naturally; you're simply wrapping up your baby to provide the snug and oh-so-blissful feeling of being back in the womb. To help you and your baby get to the point at which you both enjoy the advantages of swaddling, I wrote this book to be an informative, concise, and fun guide. Let's be honest, no mother of a newborn would have time for anything longer than this book!

You will learn all the hows and whys of swaddling, plus a few surprising facts and anecdotes that will help paint a more complete picture of an ancient practice that is suddenly making a big comeback in the United States and many other countries around the globe. Swaddling has been on a hiatus since the late 1700s in America.

What follows are some of my thoughts on swaddling, told from my personal perspective as a veteran mum of three beautiful girls, plus some interesting facts about the history and practice of swaddling. I've also included comments from several pediatric experts who help to explain the science behind swaddling and its effect on a child's development.

As I gathered research and interviewed experts, many people questioned whether I could write an entire book on swaddling. My response to them is between these pages. I think the

> ## If you are reading this book before the arrival of your first little one, brace yourself for the unexpected.

subject of swaddling is worth so much more than a few paragraphs in a 200-page baby care book. I think the practice of swaddling is so important that I put pen to paper (well, keyboard to flat screen) to impress upon new parents the value of swaddling and the importance of being patient until finding a technique and routine that feels right both to you and your baby.

Believe me, I understand firsthand all the anxieties and frustrations a new mother feels, but swaddling need not be one of them. Don't turn your back on swaddling before giving it a real chance — stick with it. It really does work and will become as routine as changing a nappy or burping your baby. And to put that in context, if you are anything like I am, before I became a mother, changing a nappy was as foreign to me then as lazing in bed on a Sunday morning with a cup of tea and the newspaper is to me now.

Elizabeth, 2 months

changing the world

one

muslin wrap at a time

And she brought forth her firstborn son, and wrapped him in swaddling clothes, and laid him in a manger; because there was no room for them in the inn.

Bible, King James version, Luke 2:7

As you read this, a swaddled baby is sleeping soundly in Sydney, another is letting out a drowsy sigh in London, and a third is cooing before drifting into a long slumber in New York.

Today, infants around the world are being comforted and coaxed into a restful sleep in much the same way babies were ushered to sleep in ancient Rome, Greece, Egypt, and China. They are being snuggly wrapped in a blanket until their bodies resemble an oversized cocoon and lulled to sleep feeling safe, secure, and comfortable.

I believe that all babies like to be swaddled. If you do not agree, think back to your first peek at a hospital nursery. There, in silent slumber, were dozens of newborns of all shapes and sizes, from myriad backgrounds, all starting out life in the same way—wrapped up as tight little bundles of joy.

Swaddling is a common bond among maternity nurses and midwives the world over because it replicates a universal feeling of security that all babies recognise, say experts. In other words, swaddling works because it feels good and familiar.

In fact, many experts believe that swaddling reproduces the snug, calming environment of the womb, which is in sharp contrast to the noisy, bright, wide-open world into which babies are thrust at birth. What a way to enter the world, via shock therapy!

Some psychologists, including W.R.D. Fairbairn in his book *Psychoanalytic Studies of the Personality*, claim that being born could very well be one of the most traumatic experiences in a person's life. Think about the transition involved in birth. Tiny newborns are yanked from the blissful state of the womb where everything they could possibly want is provided without asking, and any shock is immediately absorbed and diffused by his or her mother's body. Compare that environment to the chaos we know as life, where the first order of business for babies is to gasp for air as they emerge from the womb. It's no wonder babies can't wait to get back to the security of a swaddle.

Babies may not be the only ones feeling uneasy when it comes to birth. First-time mums, and mums of two, three, four or more children all feel the pressure of parenthood. When I fell pregnant for the first time I remember feeling snowed under by advice and inundated by facts and figures from experts and veteran mums, until I felt like my head would explode. When

Anais was born, I was petrified, and tired, and overworked, and stressed out—and my first baby had only been on the planet for 72 hours. What was life going to be like when I brought her home and it was just three first timers, my husband, my baby, and moi?

I believe that all babies like to be swaddled.

I was sure I was ill-equipped for motherhood and believed that everyone knew more and was better at child rearing than I was. One day I felt like I wasn't reading enough; the next day I felt like I was reading too much. I was taking advice from everyone who offered it—my family, friends, doctors, nurses, and lactation

consultants. I was desperate for guidance, but suffering from information overload. During that time, I would have stood on my head and sung *Baa, Baa Black Sheep* if someone had told me that it would help me get my life back. In all honesty, I'm tired just thinking about that time of my life.

My point is this: I've been in your shoes — or your old trackie pants, as the case may be — and I survived. I believe a big part of what got me through the transition to motherhood was swaddling.

I know that every mum and every baby is different, but I truly believe that the comfort and security babies feel when they are swaddled is universal. More importantly, when your baby slips into a restful full night's sleep, you can do the same. All my daughters were sleeping 10 to 12 hours a night by the time they were 12-weeks-old, and I know their good sleep habits had a lot to do with swaddling.

it's all routine

Perhaps the most important thing to remember about swaddling is that it is not difficult. It just requires a little time and patience to become comfortable with the technique. A happily swaddled baby does not have to involve Velcro® fasteners or a series of complex folds and tucks, which is what some books and professionals claim. It is much simpler than that.

Keep in mind that swaddling is not about precision, but rather it's about establishing a bedtime routine for your baby. It is also a time to relax and enjoy your baby's company, not something to dread. Again, the key to the entire experience is to keep the bedtime swaddling ritual consistent, so it eventually becomes a sleep trigger for the baby after a few weeks. It's also important to start swaddling your little one as soon as he or she comes home, because being wrapped will be a familiar feeling. That's because nurses and midwives swaddle newborn babies immediately after they are born, and since babies love and thrive on routines, a snug familiar wrap will help them adjust to their new surroundings.

The bedtime swaddling ritual I used was pretty straightforward. After feeding my daughters half their milk, I would bathe and dry them, bring them to their room to put on

sleep on his or her back to make sure breathing is not impaired.

I started off with the basic swaddle and moved to the Aussie swaddle (see Chapter 3) when my girls reached about three months. The Aussie swaddle gives babies the room to bring their hands up near their face, in case the baby wants to suck on their fist or fingers as they drift off to sleep. Sucking is a self-soothing reaction for most babies; however, reaching for a block of Jacques Torres dark chocolate is mine.

> Sucking is a self-soothing reaction for most babies; however, reaching for a block of Jacques Torres dark chocolate is mine.

their nappy and dress them in their pajamas. Next I would dim the lights for the second half of their milk whilst my sound machine played a lullaby. I would burp them, swaddle them, tell them that I loved them and to "suenos con los angelitos" (translation: "dream with the little angels"—my husband is Chilean), then change the sound machine to the white-noise setting, and place them in their cot to sleep. Always remember to place your baby to

By repeating the ritual religiously every night at the same time for about six weeks, the swaddling became a true sleep trigger. My daughters welcomed the feeling of being snuggly wrapped and responded to it as a cue to relax their little minds and bodies and drift off to a peaceful sleep. Soon after, I was able to use the swaddle to comfort my babies when they were overtired and cranky, or out-of-sorts because they were off their normal schedule. The swaddle was also a signal to my babies that it was time for a nap.

Some babies will take to their parents' swaddling ritual straight away, whilst others will fuss until the swaddle feels right. My swaddling recipe always included using a wrap made of a lightweight fabric so the baby did not overheat, and one that was large enough to securely swaddle the girls. I always like wraps that are more than 44-inches square. Also, the fabric had to have a slight stretch quality, so the swaddle was tight, but not restrictive.

I know what you are thinking. The description of my swaddling blanket sounds like a shameless plug for aden + anais® products. But it really is the other way around. Like most Australians, I was reared on muslin cotton swaddling blankets because of all the reasons I named above. I advocate the use of muslin swaddling blankets not because I sell

them, but rather I sell them because I wouldn't think of using anything else on my babies.

To be sure, I am not the only one who swears by muslin. When I had my second daughter, Lourdes, we had just received our first prototype of the product. I took the newly minted swaddling blankets with me to the hospital so I could wrap her in muslin from day one.

However, by the time I was ready to bring Lourdes (or Lulu as she is affectionately known) home, my muslin wraps had disappeared. It turns out that the maternity nurses were absconding with them because they worked better than the hospital-issued blankets. That's when I cut a deal with the nurses. "Spread the word," I said, "and you can keep the wraps." The rest, as they say, is "herstory."

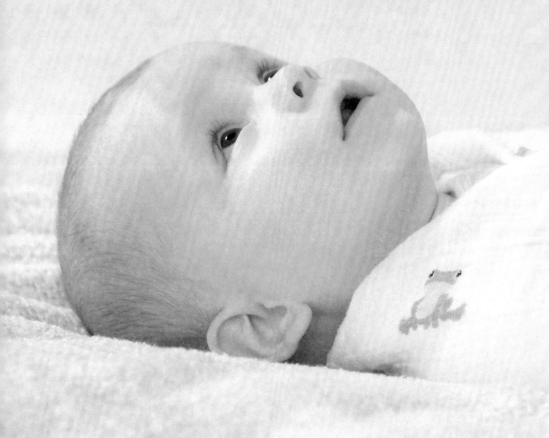

Nicholas, 5 months

back
and
better
than ever

The questioning spirit is the rebellious spirit.
A rebellion is always either a cloak to hide a prince,
or the swaddling wrapper of a new rule.

Catherine de Medici Expliquée, Honoré de Balzac

I am tempted to tell you that swaddling is the best thing since sliced bread, but it is much older than sliced bread. The ancient practice of swaddling has been a mainstay of child rearing around the globe and throughout the ages.

Some archaeologists claim that swaddling dates back to 4000 BC, during a time when mothers from nomadic tribes in Central Asia strapped swaddled babies to boards and carried the infants on their backs. Swaddled and boarded babies were a necessity for migratory mothers who were constantly on the go (not unlike modern mums) and who almost always needed both hands to harvest a moveable feast for the tribe.

Ancient child care in the Orient included one of the earliest documented uses of something called swaddling bands. These bands were strips of cloth used to tightly bind swaddled infants in positions that would supposedly straighten their backs and limbs—a draconian measure that still stigmatises the modern practice of swaddling to some extent. The use of restrictive swaddling bands was so common in ancient China that an infant who was not swaddled with ties was considered to be abandoned.

Evidence of swaddling can be seen throughout history. Discoveries made at various archaeological digs tell us that parents living in ancient Egypt, Greece, and Rome swaddled their infants. For example, votive statues of swaddled babies were unearthed in the tombs of Roman women. Meanwhile, the same types of swaddled statuettes were found near temples honoring the Greek god Amphiaraus, the mythological scion who inherited his father's gift of healing.

Early Greek texts say that Hippocrates, known as the father of medicine, lectured his students about the Egyptian practice of swaddling. And nearly four hundred years later, the second-century physician Soranus (I know, I laughed, too), who is widely believed to be the first gynecologist, instructed mothers and midwives in the art of swaddling.

Swaddling wasn't always associated with a refreshing bath and lullaby, though. In his influential text on obstetrics and gynecology, Soranus made a point of rejecting the ancient Greek and Germanic practice of swaddling

newborns before placing them in hollow logs to straighten out their backs and limbs. In the same book, he discouraged the practice of bathing babies in urine, which was warmer than available water. I'm pretty sure if I had been a toga-wearing ancient Greek mum, I would have agreed with Doctor Soranus.

Whether parents used the popular hollow tree stump method or not, swaddling backboards remained popular for some time,

Evidence of swaddling can be seen throughout history.

used often during the Middle Ages (from 600 AD through the early 1500s AD), according to historian Lloyd Demause, who wrote about swaddling in *Foundations of Psychohistory*. Swaddling backboards were also common in North America, as Native American tribes used what we commonly call papooses for their infants. Papooses were used until the babies were about six-months-old.

> Some swaddling clothes were said to have mystical powers...

Some swaddling clothes were said to have mystical powers, as was the case of the blanket used to bundle the baby who eventually became King James III of Scotland. In 1452, James was born and wrapped in a blanket that was handed down the royal line from Queen Margaret of Scotland. According to historical accounts, upon Margaret's death in 1093, her chemise was declared a royal amulet—a good luck charm of sorts—and passed down to future generations to protect them from harm.

The royal undergarment was eventually sewn into a swaddling blanket for baby James. Although he was said to be a lousy king, James was a big fan of swaddling, and historians claim that his children were swaddled quite elaborately, famously wrapped in several layers of clothing, blankets, and bands of the finest materials.

bad wrap

Swaddling as a necessity (carrying a baby whilst gathering food) or as a misguided medical procedure (straightening backs and limbs) has caused some confusion about the modern practice. As a result, some parents may shy away from swaddling because they "heard" that the practice was suspect. So, let me set the record straight. The modern practice of wrapping babies in swaddling blankets is a far cry from foolish practices of the past that seemed closer to torture than child care.

For most countries, however, the seventeenth century marked a sea change for swaddling. By that time, a handful of doctors, philosophers, and teachers—including John Locke, Jean-Jacques Rousseau, and Jonathan Richardson—led campaigns against abusive treatment of children that included criticism of horrible swaddling techniques. Enlightened minds prevailed, and instead of trying to "break" children to build them up in an adult's image, society began to acknowledge that children actually were diminutive individuals who were entitled to human rights.

Thankfully, bad swaddling habits were exorcised from many cultures by the 1800s, when the practice of swaddling to immobilise infants was abandoned. By that time, loose clothing was fast coming into fashion, including the first "children's napkins," or nappies, as well as loose-fitting, long-sleeved undershirts that opened down the front.

The bizarre history of swaddling may be one reason the practice is sometimes misunderstood by modern parents and caregivers who are unfamiliar with baby bundling. Somewhere in the back of their minds, these mums and dads may have heard about swaddling bands or the ancient Greek special log treatment and are now puzzled by the idea of wrapping up their babies. However, don't equate these strange swaddling deeds of the past with today's swaddling renaissance, because babies and parents couldn't be happier with their cozy bundling. The proof is in the swaddle.

Take a look at the faces of swaddled babies. They are content, happy, peaceful, serene.

As soon as the swaddle was on my girls, they would almost instantly close their eyes, knowing it was time to relax and sleep. Once I established a bedtime swaddling ritual, I found that my girls responded to the swaddle for their daytime naps, too, because a snug swaddle sent a signal to my babies that it was time to rest for a while. I only wish someone would invent an adult swaddle for me, because I would be first in line to buy one and wrap myself up for a nap, say around 3:00 in the afternoon.

comeback kid

Earlier I mentioned that we are in the midst of a renaissance, and that is particularly true of the United States, where swaddling is making a big comeback.

Today, it is rare if an American baby is not swaddled shortly after being born. Nurses and midwives almost immediately swaddle newborn babies [as] "standard operating procedure" in maternity wards.

Today, it is rare if an American baby is not swaddled shortly after being born. Nurses and midwives almost immediately swaddle newborn babies in what California pediatrician Dr. Loraine Stern calls "standard operating procedure" in maternity wards. Also, there is anecdotal evidence suggesting that North American parents are swaddling their infants for at least three or four months, with many bundling up their bubs until they reach their first birthday. I swaddled my girls,

Anais, Lourdes, and Arin, until they were six-months-old, when they began to outgrow the swaddle. At that point, I weaned them off swaddling and into sleeping bags (I talk about this more in Chapter 6).

Furthermore, Stern, a professor of pediatrics at the University of California Los Angeles Medical School, and the editor of the *American Academy of Pediatrics Guide to Your Child's Nutrition*, told me that she has recommended swaddling to parents who are having trouble putting their infants to sleep.

This leads me to Dr. Harvey Karp, the famed American pediatrician, who in 2003 published the wildly popular baby care book, *The Happiest Baby on the Block*, which touted the magical qualities of swaddling for, among other things, soothing crying babies and lulling them to sleep. Thank you, Dr. Karp!

Of course, there is more to a swaddle than meets the eye. In his first book, Dr. Karp explains that swaddling triggers a "relaxation" mechanism in infants that helps soothe them. Swaddling is just one technique Dr. Karp discusses regarding how to help babies adjust to life outside of the womb. However, the practice figures prominently in the book, held up as one of the all-important "five S's" parents need to use to soothe even chronic criers. The other S's are side/stomach position (when holding a baby), shushing sounds (this is where the sound machine comes in handy), swinging, and sucking.

I swaddled my daughters right from the get-go, so within a few weeks of bringing them home from the hospital, swaddling was part of their bedtime ritual. They all knew that once my husband or I swaddled them, it was time for bed.

Dakota, 4 months

bundle
of
joy

Bye, baby bunting,
Father's gone a-hunting,
Mother's gone a-milking,
Sister's gone a-silking,
And brother's gone to buy a skin
To wrap the baby bunting in.

Mother Goose, traditional nursery rhyme

The beauty of swaddling is in its simplicity. Without using specially-shaped blankets, Velcro® fasteners, or pins, the basic swaddle can be as easy as one, two, three, four.

Yes, it is a quick four-step sequence of folds and tucks that requires nothing more than a large blanket made of light breathable material and two loving hands. Of course, swaddling can be more involved. I recently talked with Dr. Bradley Thach, a professor of pediatrics and a specialist in newborn medicine at Washington University's School of Medicine, about swaddling. During our conversation, he described a more complex swaddling technique used by grandmothers from Afghanistan, Turkey, and Albania that uses three blankets. He saw this triple swaddle up-close when he invited the matriarchs to the pediatric research lab he runs with colleague Kathleen Harris at Washington University in St. Louis. The lab is involved in studies related to infant apnea, breathing development, sudden infant death syndrome (SIDS), and infant sleep physiology.

The grandmothers used three swaddling cloths—one for the baby's arms, one for the legs, and one to wrap the little bundle together. Some of the ladies used a cross-binding technique (like a shoelace) to bundle the infant, the way the baby Jesus is depicted in many paintings. I am sure the triple swaddle suits these grandmas just fine. But I don't like to make swaddling any more complicated than it has to be, so I stick to one large, lightweight blanket and a tight tuck. I'm a big proponent of a tight swaddle. All three of my daughters loved it.

Over the next few pages, I've laid out step-by-step instructions for two swaddling techniques. The first one is a basic swaddle many of my American friends use. The second is what I now refer to as the Aussie swaddle. I learned the technique whilst I was on maternity leave with Anais, back home in Sydney. A wonderful Aussie nurse who worked at a baby care clinic in the suburb of Freshwater taught me the quick-and-easy alternative, and I've used it ever since.

Both the basic and Aussie swaddle work equally well, however, the Aussie swaddle is less restrictive and allows babies to bring their hands up to their faces so that they can soothe themselves by sucking on their fist or fingers—if they are so inclined. The one you choose is really just a matter of preference. That is, your baby's preference.

My experience was that by the time my girls were 10- to 12-weeks-old, they still craved the

security of a swaddle, but were also at the stage of wanting access to their hands, making the Aussie method useful. Let me show you the four easy steps to swaddling.

how to swaddle
the basic swaddle

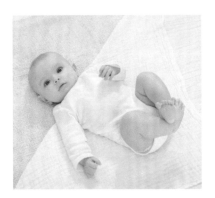

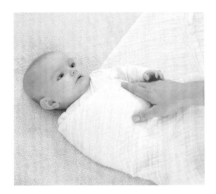

STEP 1

Lay the wrap in a diamond shape and fold the
top corner down to form a triangle. The point of
the triangle should sit about one-third of the way
into the center of the wrap. Place your baby in the
center of the folded area with his or her head just
above the fold of the wrap. Ensure that your baby's
shoulders are still below the fold. For newborns, fold
the wrap down further—approximately two-thirds
of the way into the center of the wrap—to make
the swaddle smaller.

STEP 2

Gently place your baby's right arm, slightly bent
at the elbow, flat against his or her body. Take the
left side of the wrap and bring it across your baby's
chest. Ensure that the arm is securely under the fold
of the fabric. Tuck the edge of the wrap under your
baby's body to ensure a secure swaddle.

STEP 3

Fold the bottom of the wrap up and over your baby's feet and tuck the fabric into the top of the swaddle. It is fine to skip this step and leave the fabric loose at the bottom of the swaddle if your baby prefers more freedom of movement. All my girls preferred to have their feet out at the bottom of the wrap.

STEP 4

Finally, place your baby's left arm, again, slightly bent at the elbow, flat against his or her body. Take the right side of the wrap and bring it across your baby's chest. Ensure that your baby's arm is securely under the fold of the fabric. Tuck the excess fabric of the wrap underneath your baby's body to secure the swaddle. Voila!

how to swaddle
the aussie swaddle

The Aussie method starts out the same, but changes the position of the baby's arms in Step 2.

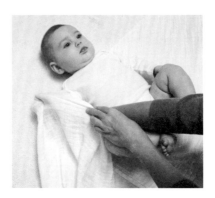

STEP 1

Lay the wrap in a diamond shape and fold the top corner down to form a triangle. The point of the triangle should sit about one third of the way into the center of the wrap. Place your baby in the center of the folded area with his or her head just above the fold of the wrap. Ensure that your baby's shoulders are still below the fold.

STEP 2

Gently tuck your baby's right arm up into the triangular fold of the wrap. Take the left side of the wrap and bring it across your baby's chest. Ensure that your baby's arm is securely under the wrap. Tuck the edge of the wrap under your baby's body to ensure a secure swaddle.

This swaddling method allows the babies to bring their hands up to their faces. It is less restrictive than the basic swaddle and is often preferred by slightly older babies.

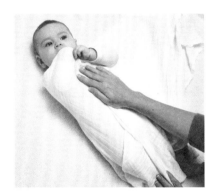

STEP 3

Fold the bottom of the wrap up and over your baby's feet and tuck the fabric into the top of the swaddle. It is fine to skip this step and leave the fabric loose at the bottom of the swaddle if your baby prefers more freedom of movement, as is the case for a number of older babies.

STEP 4

Finally, place your baby's left arm up into the triangular fold of the wrap. Take the right side of the wrap and bring it across your baby's chest. Ensure that your baby's arm is securely under the wrap. Tuck the excess fabric of the wrap underneath your baby's body to secure the swaddle.

Edward, 5 months

chapter 4

+ + + + + + + + + + + +

the
science
of
swaddling

This is the frost coming out of the ground; this is Spring.
It precedes the green and flowery spring, as mythology
precedes regular poetry. I know of nothing more purgative
of winter fumes and indigestions. It convinces me that
Earth is still in her swaddling-clothes, and stretches
forth baby fingers on every side.

Walden, Henry David Thoreau

In 2002, a trio of researchers produced scientific evidence to support what mums around the world have known for eons: Swaddled babies sleep more peacefully and for longer periods of time than babies who are not swaddled.

The results of the landmark study were published in the medical journal *Pediatrics* under the impressive title of "Spontaneous Arousals in Supine Infants While Swaddled and Unswaddled During Rapid Eye Movement and Quiet Sleep." You can look it up.

Since the study was published, it has been quoted in dozens of books and reports, magazine and newspaper articles, television and radio interviews, and on websites that discuss infant care. Bravo! This seminal study is proof that science has finally caught up to our mothers' advice.

The authors, Doctors Thach, Harris, and Claudia Gerard, all from Washington University, found that swaddling decreases the instances of babies startling themselves awake with sudden involuntary—but quite natural—arm and leg movements caused by the Moro reflex (or startle reflex). In their study, the researchers observed 26 healthy infants, each about 80-days-old, during normal nap times, documenting the differences between the sleep patterns of swaddled and unswaddled babies.

Put plainly, swaddled infants "sleep better," wrote the researchers in their report, adding that the babies "slept longer or with fewer arousals" when they were wrapped. Sleeping more soundly also extended the rapid eye movement, or REM, sleep (also called quiet sleep) for the babies. This deeper sleep "perhaps [helped] infants return to sleep spontaneously, which may limit parent intervention," concluded the study.

Yes, you read it right. Swaddling helps keep babies sleeping soundly for longer periods of time, and that feels like nothing short of a miracle for bleary-eyed new mums and dads who would gladly trade all their worldly possessions for a few extra hours of solid sleep.

Uninterrupted sleep is important for infants because it is during their sleeping hours that certain brain development takes place. In fact, many studies say that infants, especially newborns, spend about two-thirds of their day sleeping as a way of recharging their immune systems and physical well-being. Oh, to be

> Swaddling helps keep babies sleeping soundly for longer periods of time, and that feels like nothing short of a miracle...

able to sleep two-thirds of my Saturday away! That definitely would recharge my physical and mental well-being, too.

For little ones, sleep prepares their tiny bodies for growth and primes their brains for new development. During the first few months of their lives, my girls were never awake for more than 90 minutes at a time.

from startle to finish

In my chat with Dr. Thach, he explained some of the science behind swaddling and a baby's startle reflex. For example, he said that humans, as well as animals, take deep intermittent breaths that are crucial for proper lung function. These natural "sighs" restore lung "compliance," a technical term for stretching the lungs to keep the pulmonary system open and working. It's a kind of "sigh of relief for your lungs," he told me.

Whilst the deep breath is great for adults and babies, it can also stimulate the startle reflex, which can jerk infants out of their sleep, giving them a momentary fright. I understand this completely. I would cry, too, if something jerked me out of a great dream about winning a one-hour free shopping spree on Madison Avenue.

One way to prevent this wake-up jolt in infants—something researchers call "full arousal"—is to inhibit the startle reflex by gently restricting arm and leg movements, whilst still allowing the baby to breathe naturally and take big sighs when needed. Enter swaddling, the ancient proven practice that is just beginning to make a comeback.

Most doctors and scientists agree that the startle reflex lasts about two to four months, after which time many babies begin to gain more control over their bodies. But by that time, many swaddled babies enjoy the cozy feel of being wrapped up and also recognise swaddling as their cue for bedtime. As a result, pediatric specialists see no reason to stop swaddling simply because the startle reflex disappears.

Although no one can be absolutely sure why babies like the feeling of being snuggly wrapped, many experts speculate that a tight

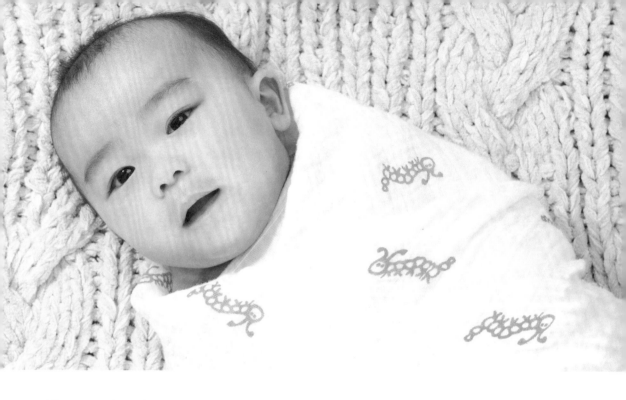

swaddle mimics the safe and secure environment of the womb. "While that theory can't be proved, it makes sense," says Dr. Stern. She contends that there was little room in the womb, and a snug swaddle reproduces that tight fit.

She describes properly swaddled babies as looking like "little burritos" when they are wrapped up tight, something you can see for yourself in any maternity ward in the country. Dr. Stern tips her hat to maternity nurses, whom she considers some of the best swaddlers bar none, for the way they wrap up dozens of babies in tight little bundles and send them off into a blissful sleep. In fact, Dr. Stern told me that many nurses advise that the tighter the swaddle, the better. Dr. Thach also commented on the tight swaddle, saying that in some cultures, fathers are considered the best swaddlers because they are stronger and can produce tighter wraps.

Although the swaddle should be snug, it should not restrict all movement, as infant development nurse Theresa Kledzik asserts in an article she published in *Contemporary Pediatrics* in 2004. She noted that swaddling should not be thought of—or used—as a restraint, but rather to help an infant self-regulate. In other words, by creating an effective swaddle, "a baby's breathing, heart rate, and color will normalise, as well as the infant's ability to transition from a fussy or crying state to a quiet awake or sleep state," concluded Kledzik in her article.

From my perspective, large muslin wraps— or other light, slightly stretchy fabrics—give parents the best of both worlds. They can produce a tight swaddle that the baby cannot easily undo, whilst allowing the baby to move and breathe. The movement is especially important if babies feel the need to raise their hands to their face and suck their fist or fingers to self-soothe.

it ain't heavy

I've never been keen on swaddling blankets made of materials heavier than muslin, especially ones that have no "give." Not only can heavy blankets cause a baby to overheat, but they can also produce what Dr. Thach refers to as the "boa constrictor" effect, meaning that the stiff blanket impedes a baby's natural breathing pattern. One way for a parent to tell if a swaddle is causing the boa constrictor effect is to monitor the baby's breathing after wrapping. If babies begin to take frequent, shallow breaths, unlike their natural breathing pattern, the swaddle is too tight, counsels Dr. Thach. All this said, the last thing you want is a loose swaddle, because it is ineffective and in some cases dangerous. Dr. Thach explained that loose bedding in the cribs of very young infants increases the risk of babies getting tangled up in the linens. In addition, swaddles that are easily undone don't work because when babies who are usually swaddled can escape the wrap, they often startle themselves awake or become restless once the security of the swaddle is missing.

"Parents that swaddle will tell you that if you don't swaddle tight enough, the baby will wriggle out of the wrap, wake up and start to cry," pediatric occupational therapist and sensory expert Cris Rowan told me. "[Parents who swaddle] are very particular about the method and tightness of their swaddles," she

> To this day, we swear that swaddling our girls is what gave us time to recuperate after long days filled with new baby duties...

added, pointing out that if the swaddle isn't "just right" parents say the baby has a restless sleep. I can vouch for Rowan's claim. My husband and I could be classified as neurotic when it came to a tight swaddle. "Tight is right" has been our motto. To this day, we swear that swaddling our girls is what gave us time to recuperate after long days filled with new baby duties, because once our babies were swaddled, they were asleep in no time.

Fiona, 3 months

the
magic
of
touch

But Phoebus Apollo plucked him up in his hands
and swathed him round in a swirling dark mist.

The Illiad, Homer

Have you ever had someone tuck you in? It feels really good to have the blankets folded under and around you.

You might think being tucked in brings me back to my childhood home, but it doesn't anymore. Now I think of my once-a-year massage, a hedonistic treat I allow myself around my birthday. The massage therapist is great at making me feel cozy and relaxed before going to work on my neck and shoulders. It's an indulgence I look forward to each year.

Cozy is a great feeling, and "it's the same for infants," contends Rowan, who has created her own developmental educational programme for children with disorders related to touch deprivation. I chatted with Rowan about how swaddling figures into the basic human need to be touched. Her theories are supported by the research of Dr. Karp, who

asserted in his book that swaddling reproduces the continuous touching and support the fetus experiences whilst in the womb. Rowan usually takes her discussion of touch a step further than Karp. She explained how very young infants need to have their tactile system desensitised so they become comfortable being touched. Otherwise, simply being held, rocked, or carried might feel similar to the way adults feel when they have the flu—very achy all over. If the developing tactile system does not receive an adequate amount of what Rowan terms "deep pressure touch stimuli," the infant can become uncomfortable with touch.

As children grow, a lack of touch may even result in developmental problems, sometimes characterised as reactive attachment disorders, behavior problems, and anxiety or depression, said Rowan. Can swaddling help? Sure, to some extent. Swaddling and holding babies increases tactile stimulation, and that comforting touch helps foster a healthy parent attachment, aids with early socialisation, and enhances a child's ability to focus and learn, according to Rowan.

Additionally, Rowan said swaddling can play an interesting role in Caesarean section births. (All of my girls were C-section births). "During natural childbirth, there is a huge desensitisation of the tactile system," as the baby moves through the birth canal, she explained. But that's not the case with C-section babies.

As the number of C-section births increased over the years, occupational therapists who worked with infants began to notice the same kind of heightened touch sensitivity in full-term C-section babies that they ordinarily associate with premature and drug-addicted infants. To help combat the touch sensitivity in these babies, therapists teach parents how to swaddle, because swaddling inhibits the body's sympathetic nervous system, which becomes more active during times of stress. In other words, swaddling a baby will induce calming effects in both healthy full-term infants, as well as in infants who are born prematurely or show signs of tactile disorders.

Rowan is not alone in touting the advantages of touch. The World Health Organization produced a 106-page study on infant care in 2004 that addressed the need for increased touch and sensory stimulation for babies as one way to boost the likelihood of healthy child development.

Connor, 4 months

enduring
questions

Hark you, Guildenstern, and you too; at each ear
a hearer. That great baby you see there is not yet
out of his swaddling clouts.

Hamlet, Act II, Scene II, William Shakespeare

"When should I stop swaddling my baby?" It is perhaps one of the most frequently asked swaddling questions new parents pose to experts and send into the blogosphere. The most frequently cited answer: "The baby will let you know."

"Most babies will tell you when they don't want to be swaddled anymore," says Dr. Thach. When they are older, stronger, or feel more comfortable outside of the swaddle, they will likely put up a terrible fuss or simply fight their way out of the swaddle and be content to sleep unbundled. When my little Houdinis began wriggling out of their swaddling blankets, I switched to sleeping bags. The bags allowed the girls to feel secure and sleep through the night, whilst eliminating the risk of having loose blankets in their crib.

As you might expect, babies reject swaddling at different ages, but it usually occurs between three and six months, the common age at which infants begin to outgrow their swaddle or develop a natural urge to move more whilst sleeping. Some mothers claim that their babies loved swaddling up until the age of one, whilst Dr. Thach told me that many cultures around the world regularly swaddle babies past the one-year-old mark. For his part, the Classical Greek philosopher Plato recommended swaddling babies until they turned two. I would have paid a great deal of money to see Plato try to swaddle my three little girls when they were two; he would have had Buckley's!

Other parents say that their babies never accepted a full swaddle, and instead preferred a half swaddle that left their arms and hands completely free. As I already mentioned, I started out with the basic swaddle, then when my girls were about three-months-old, I moved to the more liberal Aussie swaddle so they could bring their hands to their mouths. By the time my girls were six- or seven-months-old, they became comfortable with a bath, story, lullaby, and muslin sleeping bag rather than a muslin swaddle.

overheating

The other swaddling question on the minds of new parents is whether the practice can be harmful. According to both Doctors Thach and Stern, the number one risk associated with swaddling is overheating, and there are

As you might expect, babies reject swaddling at different ages, but it usually occurs between three and six months, the common age at which infants begin to outgrow their swaddle or develop a natural urge to move more whilst sleeping.

a few simple rules to follow to prevent this from happening. First and foremost, to reduce the risk of overheating, never cover a swaddled baby's face or head.

If the ambient temperature is warm or hot, or if the baby is sleeping in a particularly warm room, parents must take care not to wrap the infant in a heavy blanket. In fact, many experts recommend that swaddling be done with only lightweight blankets. Dr. Thach contends that if the blanket is thin or "sheet like" the baby should not have a problem with overheating. "People have a tendency to overdress their babies," says Dr. Stern. They don't realise that a full-term baby can control his or her own temperature as long as the ambient temperature is normal. In Australia, where the temperature regularly reaches 100 degrees Fahrenheit in the summer (the Northern Hemisphere's winter), most babies are just swaddled in a nappy in a room that is not air conditioned. To prevent overheating on warm days no matter where you live, Dr. Stern suggests dressing babies in only their nappies before swaddling with a light blanket.

Over-bundling babies on warm days is one of my pet peeves. I am very easily set off by the sight of a baby in a pram covered by a thick blanket on a warm day. At that point, it takes every bit of restraint I have not to reprimand the baby's parents. I am utterly confused by mums and dads who think it is warm enough to dress themselves in tank tops and shorts, but feel compelled to bundle the little "person" — yes folks, that's what babies are, little people — in heavy blankets. I really think socks, long sleeves, and a non-breathable wool, synthetic,

or flannel blanket might just be overkill when the temperature outside is 80 degrees Fahrenheit ... but I digress.

Keep in mind that compared to adults and older children, babies are at a disadvantage in extreme weather — whether it is too hot or too cold. Their bodies don't emit the same early warning signs that we take for granted. For example, babies don't shiver or get goose bumps, noted Dr. Stern, as "they haven't developed that mechanism yet, which often doesn't kick in until they are toddlers." Adults, on the other hand, shiver and produce goose bumps to generate more heat and reduce the surface area of the skin, respectively.

The problem for small children and babies is that they usually can't tell when they are in danger until they are already very cold or overheated. Think about blue-lipped kids who refuse to come out of the pool because they swear they're not cold. The same goes for overheating—babies must rely on their parents to protect them from harsh temperatures. And whilst swaddling usually won't affect the body temperature of a sleeping baby when the ambient temperature is average or cool, it may affect an infant on a hot day or in a warm room.

Also keep in mind that adults can kick off blankets if they feel overheated when sleeping. But a four-week-old baby doesn't have the strength or dexterity to do that, and can only wake up screaming if uncomfortable. Remember, swaddle tight, but light.

Over-bundling also is a problem in cold weather. In February 2007, the Johns Hopkins Children's Center published an article warning parents and caregivers to be "extra careful during the cold winter months, when the flu and other infections abound and the urge to bundle up babies extra warmly increases the risk of [sudden infant death syndrome]." The article, authored by sleep specialist Dr. Ann Halbower, said that "over-wrapping" can lead to overheating, even when it's cold outside.

face up, always

Another hard and fast rule to follow is that babies—whether swaddled or not—should always be placed on their backs, never on their bellies. In that position, the baby is never in danger of smothering from lying face down whilst sleeping.

Some research indicates that there is a link between SIDS and placing babies face down when putting them to sleep. SIDS is not a disease, but a diagnosis used to describe the death of a very young infant, usually less than six months of age, who has died from an unknown cause. Some theories blame this devastating syndrome on brain abnormalities that affect a baby's breathing, placing babies face down whilst sleeping, and second-hand smoke. But no research has produced definitive evidence about the root causes of SIDS.

Whilst swaddling itself does not cut down on the risk of SIDS, following proper swaddling precautions does. In their landmark report, Dr. Thach and his co-authors wrote that infants who are swaddled and placed on their backs "have a significantly lower risk for SIDS" than unswaddled infants who are placed in the same position. The decreased risk may be related to the "motor restraint of swaddling" that keeps infants from rolling over onto their bellies. Furthermore, a swaddle "prevent[s] them from getting their heads caught in loose blankets," wrote the authors.

hips and joints

Parents also question the effect swaddling may have on a baby's hip and leg development. To ease your mind, Dr. Thach recommends taking your cue from Mother Nature. That is, allow babies to settle into a natural "frog" position, so that their legs are bent at the knees. In that way the knees are separated in such a way that the hip socket can develop properly and avoid any occurrence of hip dysplasia, which is a misalignment of the hip joint. A bigger swaddling blanket allows the baby to remain in a natural position.

Moving from the hips up to a baby's arms and hands, physicians and nurses typically recommend making sure the baby's elbows are in a bent position, which again, is what comes naturally to a baby.

Raylee, 6 months

the swaddling cheat sheet

Under every grief and pine
Runs a joy with silken twine.
The babe is more than swaddling bands;
Throughout all these human lands.

Auguries of Innocence, William Blake

Here's a short and simple guide to what every parent
and caregiver needs to know about swaddling:

- Swaddling has withstood the test of time. It's an ancient practice and is currently used all over the world.

- Most hospitals and birth centers swaddle babies immediately after they are born.

- Swaddling is believed to simulate the environment of the womb, and as a result it creates a sense of familiarity, comfort, and security for newborn babies.

- Swaddling inhibits the startle reflex so that sleeping babies are prevented from waking up.

- Swaddling is about establishing a routine for your baby, not about a precise wrapping technique.

- Your baby's bedtime routine should involve the same steps (for example, feeding, bathing, swaddling, lullaby), preferably at the same time every night.

- Eventually, swaddling will become a sleep trigger for your baby, who will instantly calm when he or she is snuggly wrapped in a swaddle blanket. The process will send your baby off into a peaceful slumber. Your relaxation follows!

- When swaddling your baby, always use a large, lightweight breathable blanket that is made of a slightly stretchy fabric. This allows you to produce a secure wrap without restricting breathing.

- Swaddling is not difficult—it just takes a little persistence and patience.

- A snug swaddle helps prevent the baby from escaping the wrap, thereby avoiding the risk of the baby getting tangled up in a loose blanket.

- A swaddled baby's legs and arms should be bent in a natural position. For example, a baby's legs should be bent at the knees like a frog. See the picture of Dakota (page 32) on Step 1 of the basic swaddle method.

- After two to three months or so, babies may want to bring their hands up to their face to suck on their fist and fingers. If this is the case, a less restrictive swaddling technique—like the Aussie swaddle method—may be used.

- Never over-bundle a baby, especially in warm weather or in a warm room. The baby could overheat.

- Put babies to sleep on their backs, and never lay down a swaddled baby on his or her belly, as this could restrict the infant's breathing.

- Never cover the face of a swaddled baby, as this could also restrict breathing.

- Enjoy swaddling. It is a time for both you and your baby to relax and enjoy being together.

- A content, swaddled baby is truly one of life's great joys. I know. I have been blessed with three of them.

Fergus, 7 months

the aussie -to- american english translator

Miracles are the swaddling clothes of infant churches.

The Church History of Britain, Vol. III, Thomas Fuller

Hailing from Australia, and writing a book that will debut in the United States, I ran into some early translation problems with my American colleagues and editors.

After spending more than a decade in New York, I should have realised that I was going to send the Microsoft® Word™ spell-check programme into an apoplectic fit every time I wrote about bubs or suggested placing babies in a pram.

To ease the minds of anxious readers who have more important things to think about than translating Oz English to American English, here's a handy guide to help you navigate *swaddle love*, as well as a few extra words that will help with any conversation you may have with mates from Down Under:

An Australian Would Say	An American Would Say
Arvo	Afternoon
Bikkie	Cookie
Boot	Trunk
Brekkie	Breakfast
Bub	Baby
Buckley's	No chance
Cheeky	Naughty
Chokkie	Chocolate

An Australian Would Say	An American Would Say
Cot	Crib
Cranky	Angry
Cuddle	Hug
Dummy	Pacifier
Dobber	Tattletail
Fairy floss	Cotton candy
Flannel	Washcloth
Fortnight	Two Weeks
Hubby	Husband
Kindie	Kindergarten
Lollie	Candy
Loo	Bathroom
Mates	Friends
Mozie	Mosquito
Mum	Mom
Nappy	Diaper
Pram	Stroller
Sleeping bag	Sleep sack/wearable blanket
Ta	Thank you
Take-away	Take-out
Trackies	Sweat pants
Wee	Pee
Wrap	Blanket

Edward, 5 months

alternative
universe

The Lady to the Nurse: How now, how doth
the child? ... Unswaddle him, undo his swaddling
bands ... Pull off his shirt, thou art pretty and
fat my little darling.

The French Garden, Claudius Hollybrand and Peter Erondell

Nothing teaches you to become resourceful — in a hurry —
like becoming a new parent.

Probably to the chagrin of many product designers and manufacturers, I've used clothes pins as chip bag clips, timed hard-boiled eggs with the microwave popcorn setting, used shower curtain liners as a drop cloth for finger painters, and turned those little Chinese sauce packets that come with take-away orders into tiny ice packs by throwing them into the freezer (the whole concept of a tiny ice pack is intriguing enough to take a toddler's mind off of a minor bruise). I've also found that muslin swaddling blankets are not just for swaddling anymore. Here are some alternative uses that I think are particularly useful. Put swaddling blankets to work as:

- A portable crib sheet;

- A tummy time blanket;

- A summertime picnic blanket on the grass or at the beach;

- A nursing cover for when you nurse your baby in public;

- A large burp cloth folded and draped over your shoulder — the large size protects you, the furniture, and the floor;

- A shade for the pram to protect your baby from the sun and insects;

- A change table cover or take-anywhere changing pad to use when putting on a fresh nappy whilst on the go;

- An easy-to-carry quick-dry towel for the beach or park sprinkler.

I've used...those little Chinese sauce packets that come with take-away orders [and turned them] into tiny ice packs by throwing them into the freezer...

alternative universe

Clover, 3 months

raegan's

picks

I was not allowed to tell you before, or since, but your father was, or will be, King Uther Pendragon, and it was I myself, disguised as a beggar, who first carried you to Sir Ector's castle, in your golden swaddling bands.

The Once and Future King, T.H. White

Despite complaining about information overload, I still think
we are lucky to live during a time when mountains of information
are available if you want or need it.

Still, it's not easy sifting through truckloads of advice that are literally at our fingertips. Since this
book is aimed at easing parenthood anxieties, this section is my attempt to help you wade through
the pages upon pages of available information and come out with some useful tidbits. It's a list of
my favorite baby things.

The list is not meant to be an official endorsement or an advertisement of these books, websites,
and products, but rather just one mum (that's me) passing along some information about "stuff" that
has been invaluable to me during my nearly six years of motherhood.

books

What to Expect When You're Expecting
by Heidi Murkoff and Sharon Mazel
(Workman Publishing)

*Secrets of the Baby Whisperer: How to
Calm, Connect, and Communicate with Your
Baby* by Tracy Hogg and Melinda Blau
(Ballantine Books)

*The Contented Little Baby Book: The Simple
Secrets of Calm, Confident Parenting* by Gina
Ford (New American Library)

*The Happiest Baby on the Block: The New Way
to Calm Crying and Help Your Newborn Baby
Sleep Longer* by Harvey Karp, M.D. (Bantam)

First Meals by Annabel Karmel
(Ebury Publishing)

websites

thehappiestbaby.com   parents.com
dailycandykids.com   gocitykids.com
sleepyplanet.com   babybuggy.org

stuff
(as in... my babies and I couldn't live without)

- Nursing wear by boob®
- Skip Hop© diaper bags
- Graco® car seat/SnugRider® stroller
- Cetaphil® gentle skin cleanser
- Muslin washcloths
- Cetaphil® moisturising lotion
- Paw paw ointment
- Triple Paste® medicated ointment
- Brookstone® Tranquil Moments White Noise
  Sound Machine for Baby
- Muslin wraps
- Little Giraffe® satin and velvet security blankets

epilogue

Swaddling has been a natural part of child rearing since Biblical times, and in most cultures—whether ancient or modern—people have swaddled their infants in some shape or form, regardless of what country they call home.

I call New York and Sydney home. Australia is where I was born, raised, and educated; New York is where I live now. How did I get wrapped up in the business of swaddling, you ask? That story starts in ancient Greece with Plato, who was the first to assert that necessity is the mother of invention. Let me explain.

In 2003, I was an expectant mother from Australia—and living in the United States, half-a-world away from my family. I was about to give birth for the first time and did what any soon-to-be mum would do faced with the prospect of bringing a new life into the world. I panicked. "What am I doing so far from home? What do I know about raising children or caring for a baby?" I had no idea what great unknown was on the other side of pregnancy.

So I retreated to what was most familiar, which, relevant to this book, meant finding muslin swaddling wraps—a staple for Aussie mothers—and according to our mums, the only cloth fit for the job.

I scoured American department stores and baby boutiques for the soft, stretchy cotton wraps that our mothers used, and their mothers used, and—well, you get the picture. The muslin wraps I knew from home were light and breathable, which prevented swaddled babies from overheating. They were big and had a slight natural stretch to the fabric that made it easier to produce a snug swaddle without restricting a baby's natural breathing rhythm.

None of the swaddling blankets I found—sometimes called receiving blankets or layettes in the States—were made of muslin, and none were big enough to make the kind of baby bundles I was familiar with, having been raised in Australia. The only way to get hold of Aussie-type wraps was to send home for them, which I can tell you is not the most efficient or economical way to shop.

Before I could stop myself, I took a page from Plato's *Republic*—inventing by way of necessity— and decided to take matters into my own hands. In 2004, with about six months' worth of mothering under my belt and no small business experience, I—along with an Aussie friend who

> Before I could stop myself, I took a page from Plato's *Republic*—inventing by way of necessity— and decided to take matters into my own hands.

lived in L.A. and also just had her first baby—started our own swaddling blanket company and christened it aden + anais® after our first-born babies. We decided to manufacture washcloths and towels, too, because the soft, durable muslin was a better alternative to the coarser fabrics that were generally used to make washcloths. What baby wants to soak in a warm bath and then be bathed with a scratchy washcloth... not mine!

Since launching the first aden + anais® swaddling wraps—literally out of the boot of our cars (well, actually it was a taxi at the Upper Breast Side in New York City, but a car at the Juvenile Shop in California)—the business has grown to include organic products, a line of muslin sleeping bags for babies who have outgrown swaddling, as well as a range of multi-purpose bib/burp cloths. Today, our muslin products are sold in department stores, including Fred Segal and Barneys, as well as boutiques, including Auntie Barbara's and Bel Bambini and many others around the world. Through it all—by "all" I mean the births of my three daughters and the birth of my business—I have been guided by one steadfast belief: All babies like the feeling of being swaddled.

As a result, I've built my business based on two simple ideas:
• Swaddling makes babies and parents happy;
• A large piece of cotton muslin is the perfect swaddling material.

Writing this book has been a labour of love. It's my way of climbing up on the swaddling soapbox and announcing to all who will listen that I have found the eighth wonder of the ancient and modern world: swaddling.

My passion for muslin has been corroborated by the fact that several copy cat products are popping up around the U.S. That these companies are jumping on the muslin bandwagon as quickly as they have just serves to reinforce my initial reason for starting the business. I knew that all Aussie mums could not be wrong, and that it would only take one of us introducing muslin wraps (also called swaddles) to American mums for them to realise that outside of nappies, this was the one other baby product that parents just cannot live without.

Looking back at my journey from new mum to business entrepreneur, I admit Plato was right about necessity being the spark. After all I've learned, I believe this book is another necessity, driven by a desire and need to educate a new generation of swaddlers.

In one sense, this is a book about passing down family traditions—about 6,000 years' worth of swaddling traditions, plus the advice of my mum and sister. In another sense, it is about sharing—teaching what I know to others, and in the process learning that some things—like admitting that your mum was right only after you have kids of your own—never really change.

Happy swaddling,
Raegan
Co-founder + CEO
aden + anais®

the aden + anais swaddle love foundation™

I am not sure I believe in coincidences. Rather, I think life has a way of revealing new possibilities by drawing you into eye-opening experiences. That's what happened when I was doing research for *swaddle love*.

Whilst working on the book, my husband and I were discussing the possibility of adopting a child, and I learned that babies in orphanages around the world were being left alone, usually at night, without being held, cuddled, rocked, or hugged in any way. In fact, many babies are placed in cots during the evening hours and remain there—for periods of 12 to 15 hours at a time—without feeling the comforting touch of another human until the next day.

At the same time I was learning about certain practices in some orphanages, my book research was providing me with information about touch deprivation in children. Medical

> Medical research shows that if babies are denied regular, physical touch during the first few years of their lives, brain development is adversely affected.

research shows that if babies are denied regular, physical touch during the first few years of their lives, brain development is adversely affected.

As more information about touch deprivation came my way, I became passionate about finding a "fix" to this heart-wrenching and now scientifically acknowledged issue. That's why I started the aden + anais swaddle love foundation™. The foundation's goal is to help keep orphanages all over the world properly staffed.

Specifically, the foundation will provide funding so these institutions can hire enough women to care for and watch over babies who cry out during the night or need to be soothed during the day. The extra helping hands will be there to console infants and toddlers when they need a hug, or to reassure babies—with a simple touch of a hand—that someone is near and they will not be left alone to cry and settle themselves night after night.

All babies need and deserve the experience of healthy human touch, and that is the guiding principle behind the aden + anais swaddle love foundation™, which, in association with The Foundation for Tomorrow, and the great work it already does, is reaching out to ensure that no orphaned child is denied the most basic of human connections—touch. To that end, a percentage of my personal royalties generated by this book will be donated directly to the aden + anais swaddle love foundation™ in the hope that it will make a significant difference in many babies' lives.

endnotes

Chapter 1

Stern, Loraine, MD. Clinical professor of pediatrics, University of California Los Angeles Medical Center. Practicing pediatrician, Valencia Pediatrics Assn, Valencia, Calif. Interview, Oct. 14, 2008.

Meltz, B.F. "Methods mimic the womb for calmer babies, calmer parents." *The Boston Globe* on the Web. April 10, 2006.

Fairbairn, W.R.D. *Psychoanalytic Studies of the Personality.* New York: Routledge, 1952.

Chapter 2

DeMeo, James. *Saharasia: The 4000 BCE Origins of Child Abuse, Sex-Repression, Warfare and Social Violence, In the Deserts of the Old World,* 2nd Edition. Ashland, Oregon: Natural Energy Works, 2006.

van Gulik, R.H. *Sexual Life in Ancient China: A Preliminary Survey of Chinese Sex and Society from Ca. 1500 BC till 1644 AD.* Boston: Brill, 1994.

Cleland, L., Davies, G., Llewellyn-Jones, L. *Greek and Roman Dress from A to Z.* New York: Routledge, 2007.

Frost, Nick. *Child Welfare: Major Themes Heal V1 (Major Themes in Health and Social Welfare).* New York: Routledge, 2004.

Soranus. *Soranus' Gynecology.* Temkin, O., transl. Baltimore: The Johns Hopkins University Press, 1991.

Demause, Lloyd. *Foundations of Psychohistory.* New York: Creative Roots Publishing, 1982.

Gay, Marcus. Occultopedia.com. "Amulet." Retrieved June 24, 2009. [www.occultopedia.com/amulet.htm].

Baumgarten, Linda. *What Clothes Reveal: The Language of Clothing in Colonial and Federal America.* New Haven: Yale University Press, 2003. Out of Print. Found on the Web. [http://yalepress.yale.edu/yupbooks/book. asp?isbn=0300095805].

Bates, Daniel, "Swaddling: The Age-Old Technique For Getting Your Baby To Sleep Is Making a Comeback." *The Daily Mail* on the Web. July 17, 2008.

Karp, Harvey, M.D. *The Happiest Baby on the Block: The New Way to Calm Crying and Help Your Newborn Baby Sleep Longer.* New York: Bantam, 2003.

Karp, Harvey. M.D. *The Happiest Toddler on the Block: How to Eliminate Tantrums and Raise a Patient, Respectful, and Cooperative One-to Four-Year-Old.* Revised edition. New York: Bantam, 2008.

Chapter 3

Thach, Bradley, MD. Professor of Pediatrics, Washington University in St. Louis Hospital. Practicing pediatrician, St. Louis Children's Hospital, St. Louis, Mo. Interview, Oct. 23, 2008.

Chapter 4

Gerard, C., Harris, K., Thach, B. "Spontaneous Arousals in Supine Infants While Swaddled and Unswaddled During Rapid Eye Movement and Quiet Sleep. *PEDIATRICS* Vol. 110 No. 6. December 2002.

Stern, Loraine. Interview.

Thach, Bradley. Interview.

Kledzik, Theresa. "Letter to the Editor: Colic." *Contemporary Pediatrics*. May, 2004 Vol. 21 Issue 5.

Rowan, Cris, BScOT. CEO, Zone'in Programs Inc. Sechelt, BC, Canada. Practicing pediatric occupational therapist, Sechelt BC. Interview, Oct. 8, 2008

Chapter 5

Rowan, Cris. Interview.

Karp, Harvey. [www.happiestbaby.com]. Retrieved, June 24, 2009.

World Health Organization. "The Importance of Caregiver-Child Interactions For the Survival and Healthy Development of Young Children." 2004.

Chapter 6

Thach, Bradley. Interview.

Stern, Loraine. Interview.

Johns Hopkins Children's Center on the Web. "Winter Colds, Over-Wrapping Raise the Risk of SIDS, Doctors Warn." February, 13, 2007. [http://www.hopkinschildrens.org/Winter-Colds-Over-Wrapping-Raise-Risk-of-SIDS.aspx].

Raegan Moya-Jones lives and works in Brooklyn, New York, with her husband and three daughters. She is a firm believer of truth in advertising, and therefore would like to point out to all the mums that pick up this book that it is only through the master work of Marko the photographer and Carl the photo retoucher that she stares back from this page bright-eyed and wrinkle-free.

aden + anais®

Made for baby. Designed for you.™

At aden + anais®, we've brought the comfort of muslin together with great design to create a line of baby products as stylish as they are soothing, and as versatile as they are beautiful.